TO-DAY AND TO-MORROW SERIES

PERSEUS, *or of Dragons.*
By H. F. Scott Stokes, M.A.
A diverting little book, chock-full of ideas. Mr. Stokes' dragon-lore is both quaint and various.—*Morning Post.*

PROTEUS, *or The Future of Intelligence*
By Vernon Lee
A consideration of the real nature of intelligence, which the author believes to be a modern quality.

THAMYRIS, *or Is There a Future for Poetry?*
By R. C. Trevelyan
The author, himself a poet, reviews the possibilities of development which lie before modern poetry, with conclusions which are not those of an optimist.

PROMETHEUS, *or Biology and the Advancement of Man*
By H. S. Jennings
A consideration of the problems of heredity and environment.

PARIS, *or The Future of War*
By Captain B. H. Liddell Hart
A companion volume to *Callinicus,* reviewing the possible methods of future war, other than gas or chemical instruments.

PEGASUS, *or Problems of Transport*
By Colonel J. F. C. Fuller
An account of "cross-country" vehicles which will achieve a revolution as great as that caused by the railway.

HEPHAESTUS, *or The Soul of the Machine*
By E. E. Fournier d'Albe
A study of the relations between man and his machines. It is vigorous and original in point of view.

TIMOTHEUS, *or The Future of the Theatre*
By Bonamy Dobrée
A forecast of the possibilities of the theatre in the future.

THRASYMACHUS, *or The Future of Morals*
By E. M. C. Joad
A stimulating book by a well known author who thinks along practical, forward-looking lines.

PYGMALION, *or The Doctor of the Future*
By Dr. R. McNair Wilson
A book that sounds the human ~~~~~~~~~~~~~~ ame time takes up in simple, un~~~~~~~~~~~ ical issues.

LYCURGUS, *or The F~~~~~*
By E. S. P. Haynes
Deals with urgently needed a~~~~~

MIDAS, *or The Future o~~~~~*
By C. H. Bretherton
An impartial criticism by an ou~~~~~ who has lived in America for ten years.

E. P. DUTTON & COMPANY

ICARUS
OR
THE FUTURE OF SCIENCE

ICARUS

OR

The Future of Science

BY

BERTRAND RUSSELL

New York

E. P. DUTTON & COMPANY

681 Fifth Avenue

Printed in the United States of America

ICARUS

OR

THE FUTURE OF SCIENCE

I. INTRODUCTORY

Mr. Haldane's *Daedalus* has set forth an attractive picture of the future as it may become through the use of scientific discoveries to promote human happiness. Much as I should like to agree with his forecast, a long experience of statesmen and governments has made me somewhat sceptical. I am compelled to fear that science will be used to promote the power of dominant groups, rather than to make men happy. Icarus, having been taught to fly by his father Daedalus, was destroyed by his rashness. I fear that the same fate

[5]

may overtake the populations whom modern men of science have taught to fly. Some of the dangers inherent in the progress of science while we retain our present political and economic institutions are set forth in the following pages.

This subject is so vast that it is impossible, within a limited space, to do more than outline some of its aspects. The world in which we live differs profoundly from that of Queen Anne's time, and this difference is mainly attributable to science. That is to say, the difference would be very much less than it is but for various scientific discoveries, but resulted from those discoveries by the operation of ordinary human nature. The changes that have been brought about have been partly

[6]

good, partly bad; whether, in the end, science will prove to have been a blessing or a curse to mankind, is to my mind, still a doubtful question.

A science may affect human life in two different ways. On the one hand, without altering men's passions or their general outlook, it may increase their power of gratifying their desires. On the other hand, it may operate through an effect upon the imaginative conception of the world, the theology or philosophy which is accepted in practice by energetic men. The latter is a fascinating study, but I shall almost wholly ignore it, in order to bring my subject within a manageable compass. I shall confine myself almost wholly to the effect of science in enabling us to gratify our passions more freely, which

has hitherto been far the more important of the two.

From our point of view, we may
divide the sciences into three groups:
physical, biological, and anthropological. In the physical group I include chemistry, and broadly speaking
any science concerned with the pro-
perties of matter apart from life. In
the anthropological group I include
all studies specially concerned with
man: human physiology and psychology
(between which no sharp line can be
drawn), anthropology, history, sociology, and economics. All these studies
can be illuminated by considerations
drawn from biology; for instance,
Rivers threw a new light on parts of
economics by adducing facts about
landed property among birds during

the breeding season. But in spite of their connection with biology—a connection which is likely to grow closer as time goes on—they are broadly distinguished from biology by their methods and data, and deserve to be grouped apart, at any rate in a sociological inquiry.

The effect of the biological sciences, so far, has been very small. No doubt Darwinism and the idea of evolution affected men's imaginative outlook; arguments were derived in favour of free competition, and also of nationalism. But these effects were of the sort that I propose not to consider. It is probable that great effects will come from these sciences sooner or later. Mendelism might have revolutionized agriculture, and no doubt some similar theory will do so sooner or later. Bacteriology may enable us to exterminate our enemies by disease. The study of heredity may in time make eugenics an exact science, and perhaps we shall in a later age be able to determine at will the sex of our children. This would probably lead to an excess of males, involving a complete change in family institutions. But these speculations belong to the future. I do not propose to deal with the possible future effects of biology, both because my knowledge of biology is very limited, and because the subject has been admirably treated by Mr. Haldane.[1]

The anthropological sciences are those from which, *a priori*, we might have expected the greatest social effects, but

[1] See his *Daedalus, or Science and the Future,*

hitherto this has not proved to be the case, partly because these sciences are mostly still at an early stage of development. Even economics has not so far had much effect. Where it has seemed to have, this is because it advocated what was independently desired. Hitherto, the most effective of the anthropological sciences has been medicine, through its influence on sanitation and public health, and through the fact that it has discovered how to deal with malaria and yellow fever. Birth-control is also a very important social fact which comes into this category. But although the future effect of the anthropological sciences (to which I shall return presently) is illimitable, the effect up to the present has been confined within fairly narrow limits.

ICARUS

One general observation to begin with. Science has increased man's control over nature, and might therefore be supposed likely to increase his happiness and well-being. This would be the case if men were rational, but in fact they are bundles of passions and instincts. An animal species in a stable environment, if it does not die out, acquires an equilibrium between its passions and the conditions of its life. If the conditions are suddenly altered, the equilibrium is upset. Wolves in a state of nature have difficulty in getting food, and therefore need the stimulus of a very insistent hunger. The result is that their descendants, domestic dogs, over-eat if they are allowed to do so. When a certain amount of something is useful, and the difficulty of obtaining it is diminished, instinct will usually lead an animal to excess in the new circumstances. The sudden change produced by science has upset the balance between our instincts and our circumstances, but in directions not sufficiently noticed. Over-eating is not a serious danger, but over-fighting is. The human instincts of power and rivalry, like the dog's wolfish appetite will need to be artificially curbed, if industrialism is to succeed.

II. EFFECTS OF THE PHYSICAL
SCIENCES

Much the greatest part of the changes
which science has made in social life is
due to the physical sciences, as is
evident when we consider that they
brought about the industrial revolution.
This is a trite topic, about which I shall
say as little as my subject permits.
There are, however, some points which
must be made.

First, industrialism, still has great
parts of the earth's surface to conquer.
Russia and India are very imperfectly
industrialized; China hardly at all.
In South America there is room for
immense development. One of the

effects of industrialism is to make the world an economic unit: its ultimate consequences will be very largely due to this fact. But before the world can be effectively organized as a unit, it will probably be necessary to develop industrially all the regions capable of development that are at present backward. The effects of industrialism change as it becomes more wide-spread; this must be remembered in any attempt to argue from its past to its future.

The second point about industrialism is that it increases the productivity of labour, and thus makes more luxuries possible. At first, in England, the chief luxury achieved was a larger population with an actual lowering of the standard of life. Then came a golden age when wages increased, hours of labour diminished, and simultaneously the middle-class grew more prosperous. That was while Great Britain was still supreme. With the growth of foreign industrialism, a new epoch began. Industrial organizations have seldom succeeded in becoming world-wide, and have consequently become national. Competition, formerly between individual firms, is now mainly between nations, and is therefore conducted by methods quite different from those contemplated by the classical economists.

Modern industrialism is a struggle between nations for two things, markets and raw materials, as well as for the sheer pleasure of dominion. The labour which is set free from providing the necessaries of life tends to be more and more absorbed by national rivalry. There are first the armed forces of the State; then those who provide munitions of war, from the raw minerals up to the finished product; then the diplomatic and consular services; then the teachers of patriotism in schools; then the Press. All of these perform other functions as well, but the chief purpose is to minister to international competition. As another class whose labours are devoted to the same end, we must add a considerable proportion of the men of science. These men invent continually more elaborate methods of attack and defence. The net result of their labours is to diminish the proportion of the population that can be put into the fighting line, since more are required for munitions. This

[18]

might seem a boon, but in fact war is now-a-days primarily against the civilian population, and in a defeated country they are liable to suffer just as much as the soldiers.

It is science above all that has determined the importance of raw materials in international competition. Coal and iron and oil, especially, are the bases of power, and thence of wealth. The nation which possesses them, and has the industrial skill required to utilize them in war, can acquire markets by armed force, and levy tribute upon less fortunate nations. Economists have underestimated the part played by military prowess in the acquisition of wealth. The landed aristocracies of Europe were, in origin, warlike invaders. Their defeat by the bourgeoisie in the French Revolution, and the fear which this generated in the Duke of Wellington, facilitated the rise of the middle class. The wars of the eighteenth century decided that England was to be richer than France. The traditional economist's rules for the distribution of wealth hold only when men's actions are governed by law, i.e. when most people think the issue unimportant. The issues that people have considered vital have been decided by civil wars or wars between nations. And for the present, owing to science, the art of war consists in possessing coal, iron, oil, and the industrial skill to work them. For the sake of simplicity, I omit other raw materials, since they do not affect the essence of our problem.

We may say, therefore, speaking very generally, that men have used the increased productivity which they owe to science for three chief purposes in succession: first, to increase the population; then, to raise the standard of comfort; and, finally, to provide more energy to war. This last result has been chiefly brought about by competition for markets, which led to competition for raw materials, especially the raw materials of munitions.

III. THE INCREASE OF ORGANIZATION

The stimulation of nationalism which has taken place in modern times is, however, due very largely to another factor, namely the increase of organization, which is of the very essence of industrialism. Wherever expensive fixed capital is required, organization, on a large scale is of course necessary. In view of the economies of large scale production, organization in marketing also becomes of great importance. For some purposes, if not for all, many industries come to be organized nationally, so as to be in effect one business in each nation.

Science has not only brought about

the need of large organizations, but also the technical possibility of their existence. Without railways, telegraphs, and telephones, control from a centre is very difficult. In ancient empires, and in China down to modern times, provinces were governed by practically independent satraps or proconsuls, who were appointed by the central government, but decided almost all questions on their own initiative. If they displeased the sovereign, they could only be controlled by civil war, of which the issue was doubtful. Until the invention of the telegraph, ambassadors had a great measure of independence, since it was often necessary to act without waiting for orders from home. What applied in politics applied also in business: an organization controlled from the centre had to be very loosely knit, and to allow much autonomy to subordinates. Opinion as well as action was difficult to mould from a centre, and local variations marred the uniformity of party creeds.

Now-a-days all this is changed. Telegraph, telephone, and wireless make it easy to transmit orders from a centre: railways and steamers make it easy to transport troops in case the orders are disobeyed. Modern methods of printing and advertising make it enormously cheaper to produce and distribute one newspaper with a large circulation than many with small circulations; consequently, in so far as the Press controls opinion, there is uniformity, and, in particular, there is uniformity of news. Elementary education, except in so far as religious denominations introduce variety, is conducted on a uniform pattern decided by the State, by means of teachers whom the State has trained, as far as possible, to imitate the regularity and mutual similarity of machines produced to standard. Thus the material and psychological conditions for a great intensity of organization have increased *pari passu,* but the basis of the whole development is scientific invention in the purely physical realm. Increased productivity has played its part, by making it possible to set apart more labour for propaganda, under which head are to be included advertisement, the cinema, the Press, education, politics, and religion. Broadcasting is a new method likely to acquire great potency as soon as people are satisfied that it is *not* a method of propaganda.

Political controversies, as Mr. Graham Wallas has pointed out, ought to be conducted in quantitative terms. If sociology were one of the sciences that had affected social institutions (which it is not), this would be the case. The dispute between anarchism and bureaucracy at present tends to take the form of one side maintaining that we want no organization, while the other maintains that we want as much as possible. A person imbued with the scientific spirit would hardly even examine these extreme positions. Some people think that we keep our rooms too hot for health, others that we keep them too cold. If this were a political question, one party would maintain that the best temperature is the absolute zero, the other that it is the melting point of iron. Those who maintained any intermediate position would be abused as timorous time-servers, concealed agents of the other side, men who ruined the enthusiasm of a sacred cause by tepid appeals to mere reason. Any man who had the courage to say that our rooms ought to be neither very hot nor very cold would be abused by both parties, and probably shot in No Man's Land. Possibly some day politics may become more rational, but so far there is not the faintest indication of a change in this direction.

To a rational mind, the question is not: Do we want organization or do we not? The question is: How much organization do we want, and where and when and of what kind? In spite of a

[28]

temperamental leaning to anarchism, I am persuaded that an industrial world cannot maintain itself against internal disruptive forces without a great deal more organization than we have at present. It is not the amount of organization, but its kind and its purposes, that cause our troubles. But before tackling this question, let us pause for a moment to ask ourselves what is the measure of the intensity of organization in a given community.

A man's acts are partly determined by spontaneous impulse, partly by the conscious or unconscious effects of the various groups to which he belongs. A man who works (say) on a railway or in a mine is, in his working-hours almost entirely determined in his actions by those who direct the collective labour of which he forms part. If he decides to strike, his action is again not individual, but determined by his Union. When he votes for Parliament, party caucuses have limited his choice to one of two or three men, and party propaganda has induced him to accept *in toto* one of the two or three blocks of opinions which form the rival party programmes. His choice between the parties may be individual, but it may also be determined by the action of some group, such as a trade union, which collectively supports one party. His newspaper-reading exposes him to great organized forces; so does the cinema, if he goes to it. His choice of a wife is probably spontaneous, except that he must choose a woman of his own class. But in the education of his children he is almost entirely powerless:

they must have the education which is provided. Organization thus determines many vital things in his life. Compare him with a handicraftsman or peasant-proprietor who cannot read and does not have his children educated, and it becomes clear what is meant by saying that industrialism has increased the intensity of organization. To define this term, we must, I think, exclude the unconscious effects of groups, except as causes facilitating the conscious effects. We may define the intensity of organization to which a given individual is subject as the proportion of his acts which is determined by the orders or advice of some group, expressed through democratic decisions or executive officers. The intensity of organization in a community may then be defined as the

average intensity for its several
members.

The intensity of organization is
increased not only when a man belongs
to more organizations, but also when
the organizations to which he already
belongs play a larger part in his life,
as, for example, the State plays a
larger part in war than in peace.

Another matter which needs to be
treated quantitatively is the degree of
democracy, oligarchy, or monarchy in
an organization. No organization
belongs completely to any one of the
three types. There must be executive
officers, who will often in practice be
able to decide policy, even if in theory
they cannot do so. And even if their
power depends upon persuasion, they
may so completely control the relevant
publicity that they can always rely

upon a majority. The directors of a railway company, for instance, are to all intents and purposes uncontrolled by the shareholders, who have no adequate means of organizing an opposition if they should wish to do so. In America, a railroad president is almost a monarch. In party politics, the power of leaders, although it depends upon persuasion, continually increases as printed propaganda becomes more important. For these reasons, even where formal democracy increases, the real degree of democratic control tends to diminish, except on a few questions which rouse strong popular passions.

The result of these causes is that, in consequence of scientific inventions which facilitate centralization and propaganda, groups become more organized, more disciplined, more group-conscious, and more docile to leaders. The effect of leaders on followers is increased, and the control of events by a few prominent personalities becomes more marked.

In all this there would be nothing very tragic, but for the fact, with which science has nothing to do, that organization is almost wholly national. If men were actuated by the love of gain, as the older economists supposed, this would not be the case; the same causes which have led to national trusts would have led to international trusts. This has happened in a few instances, but not on a sufficiently wide scale to affect politics or economics very vitally. Rivalry is, with most well-to-do energetic people, a stronger motive than love of money. Successful rivalry requires organization of rival forces;

the tendency is for a business such as oil, for example, to organize itself into two rival groups, between them covering the world. They might, of course, combine, and they would no doubt increase their wealth if they did so. But combination would take the zest out of life. The object of a football team, one might say, is to kick goals. If two rival teams combined, and kicked the ball alternately over the two goals, many more goals would be scored. Nevertheless no one suggests that this should be done, the object of a football team being not to kick goals but to win. So the object of a big business is not to make money, but to win in the contest with some other business. If there were no other business to be defeated, the whole thing would become uninteresting. This

rivalry has attached itself to nationalism, and enlisted the support of the
ordinary citizens of the countries concerned; they seldom know what it is
that they are supporting, but, like the
spectators at a football-match, they
grow enthusiastic for their own side.
The harm that is being done by science
and industrialism is almost wholly due
to the fact that, while they have proved
strong enough to produce a *national*
organization of economic forces, they
have not proved strong enough to
produce an international organization.
It is clear that political internationalism
such as the League of Nations was
supposed to inaugurate, will never be
successful until we have economic
internationalism, which would require,
as a minimum, an agreement between
various national organizations dividing

among them the raw materials and
markets of the world. This, however,
can hardly be brought about while big
business is controlled by men who are
so rich as to have grown indifferent to
money, and to be willing to risk enor-
mous losses for the pleasure of rivalry.

The increase of organization in the
modern world has made the ideals of
liberalism wholly inapplicable. Liberalism, from Montesquieu to President
Wilson, was based upon the assumption
of a number of more or less equal
individuals or groups, with no differences so vital that they were willing to
die sooner than compromise. It was
supposed that there was to be free
competition between individuals and
between ideas. Experience has shown,
however, that the existing economic
system is incompatible with all forms

of free competition except between States by means of armaments. I should wish, for my part, to preserve free competition between ideas, though not between individuals and groups, but this is only possible by means of what an old-fashioned liberal would regard as interferences with personal liberty. So long as the sources of economic power remain in private hands, there will be no liberty except for the few who control those sources.

Such liberal ideals as free trade, free press, unbiased education, either already belong to the past or soon will do so. One of the triumphs of early liberalism in England was the establishment of parliamentary control over the army; this was the *casus belli* in the Civil War, and was decided by the Revolution of 1688. It was effective so long as

Parliament represented the same class from which army officers were drawn. This was still the case with the late Parliament, but may cease to be the case with the advent of a Labour Government. Russia, Hungary, Italy, Spain, and Bavaria have shown in recent years how frail democracy has become; east of the Rhine it lingers only in outlying regions. Constitutional control over armaments must, therefore, be regarded as another liberal principal which is rapidly becoming obsolete.

It would seem probable that, in the next fifty years or so, we shall see a still further increase in the power of governments, and a tendency for governments to be such as are desired by the men who control armaments and raw materials. The forms of democracy may survive in western countries, since those who possess military and economic power can control education and the press, and therefore can usually secure a subservient democracy. Rival economic groups will presumably remain associated with rival nations, and will foster nationalism in order to recruit their football teams.

There is, however, a hopeful element in the problem. The planet is of finite size, but the most efficient size for an organization is continually increased by new scientific inventions. The world becomes more and more of an economic unity. Before very long the technical conditions will exist for organizing the whole world as one producing and consuming unit. If, when that time comes, two rival groups contend for mastery, the victor may be able to introduce that single world-wide organization that is needed to prevent the mutual extermination of civilized nations. The world which would result would be, at first, very different from the dreams of either liberals or socialists; but it might grow less different with the lapse of time. There would be at first economic and political tryanny of the victors, a dread of renewed upheavals, and therefore a drastic suppression of liberty. But if the first half-dozen revolts were successfully repressed, the vanquished would give up hope, and accept the subordinate place assigned to them by the victors in the great world-trust. As soon as the holders of power felt secure, they would grow less tyrannical and less energetic. The motive of rivalry being removed, they would not work so hard as they do now, and would soon cease to exact such hard work from their subordinates. Life at first might be unpleasant, but it would at least be possible, which would be enough to recommend the system after a long period of warfare. Given a stable world-organization, economic and political, even if, at first, it rested upon nothing but armed force, the evils which now threaten civilization would gradually diminish, and a more thorough democracy than that which now exists might become possible. I believe that, owing to men's folly, a world-government will only be established by force, and will therefore be at first cruel and despotic. But I believe that it is necessary for the preservation of a scientific civilization, and that, if once realized, it will gradually give rise to the other conditions of a tolerable existence.

IV. THE ANTHROPOLOGICAL SCIENCES

It remans to say something about the future effects of the anthropological sciences. This is of course extremely conjectural, because we do not know what discoveries will be made. The effect is likely to be far greater than we can now imagine, because these sciences are still in their infancy. I will, however, take a few points on which to hang conjectures. I do not wish to be supposed to be making prophecies: I am only suggesting possibilities which it may be instructive to consider.

Birth-control is a matter of great importance, particularly in relation to the possibility of a world-government, which could hardly be stable if some nations increased their population much more rapidly than others. At present, birth-control is increasing in all civilized countries, though in most it is opposed by governments. This opposition is due partly to mere superstition and desire to conciliate the Catholic vote, partly to the desire for large armies and severe competition between wage-earners, so as to keep down wages. In spite of the opposition of governments, it seems probable that birth-control will lead to a stationary population in most white nations within the next fifty years. There can be no security that it will stop with a stationary population; it may go on to the point where the population diminishes.

The increase in the practice of birth-control is an example of a process contrary to that seen in industrialism:

it represents a victory of individual over collective passions. Collectively, Frenchmen desire that France should be populous, in order to be able to defeat her enemies in war. Individually, they desire that their own families should be small, in order to increase the inheritance of their children and to diminish the expense of education. The individual desire has triumphed over the collective desire, and even, in many cases, over religious scruples. In this case, as in most others, the individual desire is less harmful to the world than the collective desire: the man who acts from pure selfishness does less damage than the man who is actuated by "public spirit." For, since medicine and sanitation have diminished the infant death-rate, the only checks to over-population that remain (apart from birth-control) are war and famine. So long as this continues to be the case, the world must either have a nearly stationary population, or employ war to produce famine. The latter method, which is that favoured by opponents of birth-control, has been adopted on a large scale since 1914; it is however somewhat wasteful. We require a certain number of cattle and sheep, and we take steps to secure the right number. If we were as indifferent about them as we are about human beings, we should produce far too many, and cause the surplus to die by the slow misery of under-feeding. Farmers would consider this plan extravagant, and humanitarians would consider it cruel. But where human beings are concerned, it is considered the only proper course, and works advocating any other are confiscated by the police if they are intelligible to those whom they concern.

It must be admitted, however, that there are certain dangers. Before long the population may actually diminish. This is already happening in the most intelligent sections of the most intelligent nations; government opposition to birth-control propaganda gives a biological advantage to stupidity, since it is chiefly stupid people whom governments succeed in keeping in ignorance. Before long, birth-control may become nearly universal among the white races; it will then not deteriorate their quality, but only diminish their numbers, at a time when uncivilized races are still prolific and are preserved from a high death-rate by white science.

This situation will lead to a tendency

—already shown by the French—to employ more prolific races as mercenaries. Governments will oppose the teaching of birth-control among Africans, for fear of losing recruits. The result will be an immense numerical inferiority of the white races, leading probably to their extermination in a mutiny of mercenaries. If, however, a world-government is established, it may see the desirability of making subject races also less prolific, and may permit mankind to solve the population question. This is another reason for desiring a world-government.

Passing from quantity to quality of population, we come to the question of eugenics. We may perhaps assume that, if people grow less superstitious, governments will acquire the right to sterilize those who are not considered desirable as parents. This power will be used, at first, to diminish imbecility, a most desirable object. But probably, in time, opposition to the government will be taken to prove imbecility, so that rebels of all kinds will be sterilized. Epileptics, consumptives, dipsomaniacs and so on will gradually be included; in the end, there will be a tendency to include all who fail to pass the usual school examinations. The result will be to increase the average intelligence; in the long run, it may be greatly increased. But probably the effect upon really exceptional intelligence will be bad. Mr. Micawber, who was Dickens's father, would hardly have been regarded as a desirable parent. How many imbeciles ought to outweigh one Dickens I do not profess to know.

Eugenics has, of course, more ambitious possibilities in a more distant future. It may aim not only at eliminating undesired types, but at increasing desired types. Moral standards may alter so as to make it possible for one man to be the sire of a vast progeny by many different mothers. When men of science envisage a possibility of this kind, they are prone to a type of fallacy which is common also in other directions. They imagine that a reform inaugurated by men of science would be administered as men of science would wish, by men similar in outlook to those who have advocated it. In like manner women who advocated votes for women used to imagine that the woman voter of the future would resemble the ardent feminist who won her the vote; and socialist leaders imagine that a socialist

State would be administered by ideal-
istic reformers like themselves. These
are, of course, delusions; a reform,
once achieved, is handed over to the
average citizen. So, if eugenics reached
the point where it could increase
desired types, it would not be the types
desired by present-day eugenists that
would be increased, but rather the
types desired by the average official.
Prime Ministers, Bishops, and others
whom the State considers desirable
might become the fathers of half the
next generation. Whether this would
be an improvement it is not for me to
say, as I have no hope of ever becoming
either a Bishop or a Prime Minister.

If we knew enough about heredity
to determine, within limits, what sort
of population we would have, the
matter would of course be in the hands

of State officials, presumably elderly
medical men. Whether they would
really be preferable to Nature I do not
feel sure. I suspect that they would
breed a subservient population, con-
venient to rulers but incapable of
initiative. However, it may be that I am
too sceptical of the wisdom of officials.

The effects of psychology on practical
life may in time become very great.
Already advertisers in America employ
eminent psychologists to instruct them
in the technique of producing irrational
belief; such men may, when they have
grown more proficient, be very useful
in persuading the democracy that
governments are wise and good. Then,
again, there are the psychological tests
of intelligence, as applied to recruits for
the American army during the war.
I am very sceptical of the possibility of

testing anything except average intelligence by such methods, and I think that, if they were widely adopted, they would probably lead to many persons of great artistic capacity being classified as morons. The same thing would have happened to some first-rate mathematicians. Specialized ability not infrequently goes with general disability, but this would not be shown by the kind of tests which psychologists recommended to the American government.

More sensational than tests of intelligence is the possibility of controlling the emotional life through the secretions of the ductless glands. It will be possible to make people choleric or timid, strongly or weakly sexed, and so on, as may be desired. Differences of emotional disposition seem to be chiefly due to secretions of the ductless glands, and therefore controllable by injections or by increasing or diminishing the secretions. Assuming an oligarchic organization of society, the State could give to the children of holders of power the disposition required for command, and to the children of the proletariat the disposition required for obedience. Against the injections of the State physicians the most eloquent Socialist oratory would be powerless. The only difficulty would be to combine this submissiveness with the necessary ferocity against external enemies; but I do not doubt that official science would be equal to the task.

It is not necessary, when we are considering political consequences, to pin our faith to the particular theories of the ductless glands, which may blow over, like other theories. All that is essential in our hypothesis is the belief that physiology will in time find ways of controlling emotion, which it is scarcely possible to doubt. When that day comes, we shall have the emotions desired by our rulers, and the chief business of elementary education will be to produce the desired disposition, no longer by punishment or moral precept, but by the far surer method of injection or diet. The men who will administer this system will have a power beyond the dreams of the Jesuits, but there is no reason to suppose that they will have more sense than the men who control education to-day. Technical scientific knowledge does not make men sensible in their aims, and administrators in the future, will be presumably no less stupid and no less prejudiced than they are at present.

CONCLUSION

It may seem as though I had been at once gloomy and frivolous in some of my prognostications. I will end, however, with the serious lesson which seems to me to result. Men sometimes speak as though the progress of science must necessarily be a boon to mankind, but that, I fear, is one of the comfortable nineteenth-century delusions which our more disillusioned age must discard. Science enables the holders of power to realize their purposes more fully than they could otherwise do. If their purposes are good, this is a gain; if they are evil, it is a loss. In the present age, it seems that the purposes of the holders of power are in the main evil, in the sense that they involve a diminution, in the world at large, of the things men are agreed in thinking good. Therefore, at present, science does harm by increasing the power of rulers. Science is no substitute for virtue; the heart is as necessary for a good life as the head.

If men were rational in their conduct, that is to say, if they acted in the way most likely to bring about the ends that they deliberately desire, intelligence would be enough to make the world almost a paradise. In the main, what is in the long run advantageous to one man is also advantageous to another. But men are actuated by passions which distort their view; feeling an impulse to injure others, they persuade themselves that it is to their interest to do so. They will not, therefore, act in the way which is in fact to their own interest unless they are actuated by generous impulses which make them indifferent to their own interest. This is why the heart is as important as the head. By the "heart" I mean, for the moment, the sum-total of kindly impulses. Where they exist, science helps them to be effective; where they are absent, science only makes men more cleverly diabolic.

It may be laid down as a general principle to which there are few exceptions that, when people are mistaken as to what is to their own interest, the course they believe to be wise is more harmful to others than the course that really is wise. There are innumerable examples of men making fortunes because, on moral grounds, they did something which they believed to be

contrary to their own interests. For
instance, among early Quakers there
were a number of shopkeepers, who
adopted the practice of asking no more
for their goods than they were willing
to accept, instead of bargaining with
each customer, as everybody else did.
They adopted this practice because
they held it to be a lie to ask more than
they would take. But the convenience
to customers was so great that everybody came to their shops and they grew
rich. (I forget where I read this, but
if my memory serves me it was in some
reliable source). The same policy *might*
have been adopted from shrewdness,
but in fact no one was sufficiently
shrewd. Our unconscious is more
malevolent than it pays us to be;
therefore the people who do most
completely what is in fact to their

interest are those who, on moral grounds, do what they believe to be against their interest.

For this reason, it is of the greatest importance to inquire whether any method of strengthening kindly impulses exists. I have no doubt that their strength or weakness depends upon discoverable physiological causes; let us assume that it depends upon the glands. If so, an international secret society of physiologists could bring about the millennium by kidnapping, on a given day, all the rulers of the world, and injecting into their blood some substance which would fill them with benevolence towards their fellow-creatures. Suddenly M. Poincaré would wish well to Ruhr miners, Lord Curzon to Indian nationalists, Mr. Smuts to the natives of what was German South

West Africa, the American Government
to its political prisoners and its victims
in Ellis Island. But alas, the physiologists would first have to administer the
love-philtre to themselves before they
would undertake such a task. Otherwise, they would prefer to win titles
and fortunes by injecting military
ferocity into recruits. And so we come
back to the old dilemma: only kindliness can save the world, and even if we
knew how to produce kindliness we
should not do so unless we were already
kindly. Failing that, it seems that the
solution which the Houynhnms adopted
towards the Yahoos, namely extermination, is the only one; apparently the
Yahoos are bent on applying it to each
other.

We may sum up this discussion in a
few words. Science has not given men

more self-control, more kindliness, or
more power of discounting their passions
in deciding upon a course of action.
It has given communities more power
to indulge their collective passions,
but, by making society more organic,
it has diminished the part played by
private passions. Men's collective
passions are mainly evil; far the
strongest of them are hatred and
rivalry directed towards other groups.
Therefore at present all that gives men
power to indulge their collective
passions is bad. That is why science
threatens to cause the destruction of
our civilization. The only solid hope
seems to lie in the possibility of world-
wide domination by one group, say the
United States, leading to the gradual
formation of an orderly economic and
political world - government. But

perhaps, in view of the sterility of the Roman Empire, the collapse of our civilization would in the end be preferable to this alternative.